Paul Bunyan:
Hero of the
Lumber Woods

by WALLACE WADSWORTH

illustrated by RICHARD BENNETT

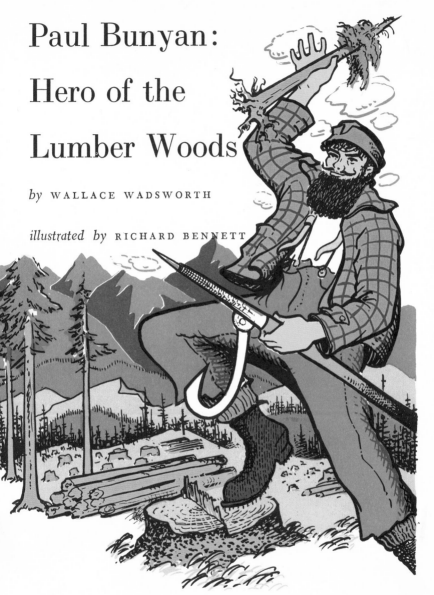

Selections from *Paul Bunyan and His Great Blue Ox*, copyright, 1926, by George H. Doran Company, and published by Doubleday & Company, Inc.

THE HERO OF THE LUMBER WOODS

In the lumber woods the winter night has settled down over the snowy forest land. The trees crackle with the cold, the ice of the lakes booms and creaks harshly in the rending grip of the frost, and far to the north those ever-restless dancers, the Northern Lights, leap and climb the sky in flickering waves of green and purple and crimson. The air stings the skin and prickles the nostrils, and no creature braves its chill save the fur-clad forest animals that slip hungrily along, restless and unseen shadows, among the trees.

Best in Children's Books

Only in the big lumber camp is there sign of warmth and comfort. There, in bunkhouse and shanty, the men have gathered together after their hard labors of the day, enjoying the companionship of one another and perhaps playing crude jokes, boasting of past deeds, or looking on laughingly while one of their number tests the mettle of another in some feat of strength. But most likely they are doing what they like best to do on a night like this, when the wind groans and whistles around the buildings and the frost noises crackle and jeer, and that is to sit back and listen while the old-timers tell over again the wonderful tales of Paul Bunyan, his blue ox Babe, and his marvelous deeds.

Paul Bunyan! the mightiest man that ever came into the woods! Never do woodsmen tire of hearing of him. Never do the stories of his tremendous labors grow old to them, for not only was he the first one of all their kind, but he was also the greatest lumberjack that ever lived, the hero of them all.

Paul Bunyan! the first and greatest logger! He is really the father of logging as it is today, for all the best methods for logging off timber were developed by him, and have been in use ever since. Not only that, but he also invented all the tools that are used by lumberjacks even today: the double-bitted ax, the grindstone, the crosscut saw, the peavy, and all the others. A very great genius was Paul, a remarkable man in every way and one well fit to be the hero of all woodsmen who have come after him.

It has been long since anyone has seen him face to face, though now and then some old-time lumberjack will admit that he has worked for Paul in one or another of his smaller camps, or that he has a friend who once knew Paul personally. It is from such men as these that the stories of the great logger's exploits have come, and since these tales of him are first-hand, so to speak, they are therefore of unquestionable truth.

Paul Bunyan was of tremendous size and strength, the strongest man that ever swung an ax. Now a lumberjack always measures things by ax-handles instead of by feet or yards—a thing will be so many ax-handles long or so many ax-handles high—and the various estimates as to Paul's size are given in this way. Accordingly, the estimate which seems most nearly correct is that Paul was so big that ninety-seven ax-handles would just barely measure him from hip to hip. This estimate is a little misleading, however, as no one is sure whether the ordinary ax-handle is meant, or one of Paul's which was seven—or perhaps it was seventy—times as long as the ordinary one. At any rate, it can easily be seen that he was no little fellow.

He had curly black hair which his loving wife used to comb for him every morning with a great crosscut saw, after first parting it nicely with a broadax, and a big black beard that was as long as it was wide and as wide as it was long. He was rather proud of this beard, and took great care of it. Several times every day he would pull up a young pine tree by the roots and use its stiff branches in combing and brushing his beard smooth.

Mrs. Paul was about of a size to match her husband. It took forty-seven grizzly bear skins to make her a fur coat—that is, one of those short ones—and one of her skirts used up more canvas than a full-rigged ship. She was affectionate and lovable, and everyone said that Paul was mighty lucky to get such a wife. The only difference between her and other women was that of size—with her the measurements were yards or rods instead of inches.

As for Babe, the Great Blue Ox, just where Paul got him has never been learned. It is thought that he secured him when but a calf, being attracted by his strange blue color, and reared him from calfhood with great care. The Ox well repaid the kindness of his master, for he was with him through all his logging operations and was continually performing labors that could not have been done in any other way. The Great Blue Ox was so strong that he could pull anything that had two ends and some things that had no ends at all, which made him very valuable at times, as one can easily understand.

Babe was remarkable in a number of ways besides that of his color, which was a bright blue. His size is rather a matter of doubt, some people holding that he was twenty-four ax-handles and a plug of tobacco wide between the eyes, and others saying that he was forty-two ax-handles across the forehead. It may be that both are wrong, for the story goes that Jim, the pet crow, who always roosted on Babe's left horn, one day decided to fly across to the tip of the other horn. He got lost on the way, and didn't get to the other horn until after the spring thaw, and he had started in the dead of winter.

The Great Blue Ox was so long in the body that an ordinary person, standing at his head, would have had to use a pair of field glasses in order to see what the animal was doing with his hind feet.

THE WINTER OF THE BLUE SNOW

It is pretty hard to give a definite date to any of the mighty deeds which Paul Bunyan performed, as only one guidepost as to time is given in all the stories that have been told of him and his exploits. This guidepost, as one may call it, is the definite mention of the winter of the Blue Snow. The snow that fell during that winter was a bright, glistening blue in color, very interesting and attractive at first, but soon growing so tiresome to the eyes that everyone was longing for the sight of some common, old-fashioned white snow again. Paul set out to find some, but he had to go clear to China before he finally found what he was looking for.

Now it is certain that all that the great logger ever did

took place either before or after the falling of the Blue Snow, and so—if it were only possible to discover the exact year during which the Blue Snowstorm occurred—all the things he did could be dated forward or backward from that time, and the definite date of their occurrence established in that way.

It is thought quite probable that the Blue Snow fell during the Year of the Two Winters, when it grew so cold that it didn't start to thaw until after it began to freeze again. They had winter all summer that year, and then in the fall it turned colder. It was so cold that one night when Paul set the coffee pot out-of-doors to cool, the coffee froze so quickly that the ice was hot.

It certainly was cold that winter, so cold that men's words froze and dropped to the ground as they were spoken; and as nobody could hear them until after they were thawed out, the lumberjacks never troubled themselves to speak mildly. Paul had all of their frozen words gathered up into a big bin, intending to haul such troublesome rubbish far away from camp and bury it, until the ever-efficient bookkeeper, Johnny Inkslinger, thought of boxing up the most explosive of all the words and selling them for blasting powder. They were very powerful, too, when a charge of them was set off all at once.

One good thing which the cold spell did was to cure all the men in camp of swearing. Whenever a man dropped a cuss-word, Paul had it picked up by a special crew for the purpose, labeled with the man's name, and stored away. When spring came and the weather began to get warm, each man that had a bale of cuss-words saved up for him had to take them all out and listen to them as they thawed. Some wonderful combinations were heard along about that time, and having to sit back and listen to their full winter's cussing all in one bunch was a most satisfactory method of curing the men of the unpleasant habit of swearing, one may be sure.

Brimstone Bill was the worst offender in camp this way—that was how he had earned his name—but after spring came that year he was just about the mildest-spoken man in seven states. He had cussed so much during the cold weather that several times he had been nearly covered up and smothered by the frozen words, and had to be pulled out from under the heap he had made. When spring came and he had to listen to all of his words as they thawed out—ah! there was some real excitement, most assuredly! He was deaf for three weeks afterwards, and he never did fully recover from the dreadful things he had heard. His experience completely cured him of swearing, however, and ever afterwards—whenever he began to feel the old inclination to say words of such nature—he would relieve his feelings with whistling instead.

The weather kept on growing colder and colder, and finally Paul heard a rumor that it had grown so cold that the Pacific Ocean had frozen over. The story seemed so unlikely that he decided to investigate for himself. "I'm going to see if it's true, what they say about the Pacific being frozen," he explained to his men, "and also I'm so homesick for the sight of some regular old white snow that I'm going to look around a little and see if I can't find some." So, followed by the faithful Babe, he set out on snowshoes to the westward.

He kept on going until he came to the ocean, but not a flake of white snow could he glimpse anywhere. The ice on the Pacific looked pretty solid, and so he struck out across it, always on the lookout for some snow that wasn't blue. He kept on and kept on, but he was far into China before he found any white snow. Proof of this may be found in the fact that nothing but white snow has ever fallen in central China. Paul was so pleased over finding what he was looking for that he loaded Babe with all he could carry and set off for home again.

When he finally got back to camp again his men all held a tremendous celebration, so pleased were they at the sight of familiar, old-fashioned snow again. Paul gave each of them a white snowball for a Christmas present that year, and most of them carried theirs around in their pockets for many years thereafter as proof that they had spent the Winter of the Blue Snow in Paul's camp. Then, if anyone doubted their word, they would just pull their white snowball out of their pocket, and there could be no further doubt about their telling the truth.

It was while the Blue Snow was on the ground that the Snow Wassets were nearly exterminated by Paul's men. The Snow Wasset is unlike other animals, inasmuch as it hibernates during the summer instead of the winter. When the snow begins to melt as the weather turns warm in the spring, this queer animal grows a pair of strong front legs that end in paws armed with big digging claws. Its color changes to green, and by the time the last snowdrift has melted away, it is denned up, all snug and sound, in a hole which it has dug in the ground. There, all covered over with moss and dirt, it sleeps away until winter comes again, when it wakes up as the first snow begins to fall. By the time drifts have begun to deepen, it has shed its legs and green fur, and has grown a brand-new winter coat. Its new fur is of the purest white and is very valuable, but as the

animal is thus so colored that it cannot be seen as it wallows about in the snow, it is very seldom ever captured.

During the Winter of the Blue Snow, however, the Wasset could be easily seen, white against the blue, and Paul's men put in much of their time that winter in hunting the squirming creatures as they played among the blue drifts. Johnny Inkslinger sold many Wasset skins in the spring, and the high price he received for these rare pelts did much toward making up to Paul for the poor cut of timber during the winter.

PAUL'S GREAT FLAPJACK GRIDDLE

It was on the banks of the Red River of the North that Paul had set up his camp, and there he assembled one of the greatest logging crews that has ever existed. So many men did he have in camp that one of his bunkhouses had a hundred and thirty-seven tiers of bunks, and the men used to go to bed with balloons and come down in the morning with parachutes. It was a pretty sight to see them early of a morning pouring out of their bunks and floating down in great clouds just about the time that the cooks were getting breakfast well under way.

No alarm clocks were needed in Paul's camp. He knew lumberjacks pretty well, Paul did, and so he just had a big pipe stretched from the cook shanty to the bunkhouses and a blower fixed in it. In the morning, when the cooks had their fires going, the victuals beginning to cook and the coffee simmering, the blower fan was turned on and the smell of breakfast blown right into the bunkhouses. Then, if a jack didn't grab his parachute and jump out of his bunk right away the camp doctor was sent to look him over, for everyone knew that he must be sick.

Paul found that feeding his many men was a good deal of a job, and especially did he find it hard to give them all the flapjacks they wanted, for they all seemed to have developed an extraordinary craving for this favorite delicacy. Since all of his men were so fond of flapjacks, he had to figure out some way to give them all they wanted, for he liked to keep his helpers satisfied.

Paul Bunyan puzzled over the problem of getting enough flapjacks for his men, and finally he ordered the camp blacksmith, Big Ole, to make him a huge griddle. So big was this griddle that the cookees greased it with telephone poles on the ends of which were tied great bunches of gunny sacks for swabs. As Paul kept on hiring more men all the time, however, it was not very long before it became far too small, and he had his problem to settle all over again.

Someone at last told him where he could get a much bigger griddle to take the place of the one that was now outgrown; but it was so large that he couldn't at first figure out how to get it to camp. Luckily it was perfectly round in shape, and though it was so thick when it was stood on edge that it made a track as wide as a wagon road and was terribly hard to lift, Paul soon thought out a way to get it to the place where he wanted it.

Being so hard pressed by the need of more flapjacks in camp, he had started working the inventive side of his brain

again, and it was at this time that he invented the electro-magnet. He and Ole made two enormous big ones so strong that when they were tested out for the first time they pulled all the axes and saws and other tools out of the hands of the men in the woods within five miles of the camp. Seeing the trouble they had caused, Paul shut off the magnets at once, but it was worse than a jigsaw puzzle sorting out all the things that had been pulled into camp. He was quite pleased, however, with such a demonstration by the magnets, for he knew that they were just the things to help him get the big griddle to where he wanted it.

Shortly before this he had bought a team of mules, Jerry and Jinny, intending to use them occasionally while he gave Babe a rest. This mule team could travel so fast, after they had had their regular feed of ten bushels of wheat apiece, that no one else could hold them in, and so Paul always had to drive them himself. He used them hitched to a big flat-bottomed wagon without wheels.

So now he harnessed his mules up, fixed his new magnets in the back of the wagon, and drove off to where the griddle was. He swung the magnets around until their strength drew the griddle right up on its edge, and then he drove off lippity-cut towards the camp. The pull of the magnets got the griddle going around so fast and following him at such a great rate of speed that he hardly knew how to stop it, for the faster the mules went, just that much faster did the griddle roll along behind trying to catch up. It was clearly impossible for him to run away from it.

When he at last passed over the spot where he wanted it, he just dropped the magnets out of the wagon and pulled up to one side to watch what would happen. The griddle rolled around and around, like a big piepan circling about on the floor as it loses its speed after someone spins it, getting nearer and nearer to where the magnets lay. It kept rolling weaker and weaker, until finally it twisted around a couple of times more, just at the place where he wanted it, and gouged out a big hole in the ground as it turned. Then it settled down, as nice as you please, right flat over the hole it had dug, and there it was at last, all ready for use and with a place for the fire underneath.

Paul then built a high fence around the griddle, and right beside it he put a couple of big buildings to hold his pancake flour. So perfectly did he have these buildings arranged that others just like them are used today as elevators for storing grain. He also invented a machine for mixing up the hot-cake batter, and had Ole make eight or ten of them, which were placed in position by the griddle. These machines of Paul's are also copied today, and any one may see many small models of them being used by paving contractors for mixing concrete.

"There now," said Paul to Sourdough Sam, the head baker of the camp, who also had charge of all the flapjack making, "there is a griddle to be proud of—a griddle which it should be a pleasure to work with."

Sam was doubtful at first, for he had had several disastrous experiments with flapjacks in the past—once having his mixing vat burst and flood the landscape for miles around with thin and sticky flapjack batter—and he was not at all optimistic about making hot cakes on the tremendous scale which Paul had just made provision for. However, after he began to get used to the new arrangements, he began also to get interested in the intricacies of flapjack making. It was not long, therefore, until he was turning out his giant hot cakes with all the artistry which he had hitherto reserved exclusively for his first love, sourdough bread. From that time on his flapjacks were so wonderful that men still talk about them, and no other griddle expert has ever been able to equal him in the preparation of this supreme delicacy.

Everything was worked out on a very definite schedule, and it was truly a wonderful sight to see the big griddle being put to its daily use. Along in the afternoon every day a gang of three hundred flapjack cooks would start getting down the flour and fixin's from the elevators, start the mixers going and stir up the batter under the careful supervision of the boss baker. Meanwhile, as the batter was being mixed, the cook-boys would have to grease the griddle. This they did by strapping whole hams or sides of bacon on their feet and skating around over the hot surface.

When the batter was all ready and the greasing done, someone on the edge would blow a whistle, and so big was the griddle that it took four minutes for the sound to get across. At this signal, all the cook-boys would skate to the edge and climb high on the fence that had been fixed for that purpose. A cook would then trip the chute from the mixers, and out would roll a wave of flapjack batter ten feet high. Any poor cook-boy who hadn't climbed out of the way, and was overtaken by the spreading batter, was in the worst kind of luck, for he would be found later in the

flapjack just like a raisin in a cake.

Paul had a hard time at first figuring out how to flip the flapjack over onto its other side so that both sides of it would be cooked the same. Everyone has, of course, seen flapjacks flipped up in the air out of a skillet, so that when they come down again they have turned completely over and the undone side has a chance to get browned in its turn. Of course the big griddle and the flapjack on it were far too heavy for any wrist to flip in the ordinary manner, and so for a while everybody had to eat flapjacks that were done only on one side. Paul tried rigging a block-and-tackle arrangement for turning the big hot cake over, but that did not work very well, and the plan was abandoned.

At last he hit on the scheme of flipping it over with dynamite, which plan worked out so well that it was used from that time on. Whenever one side of the flapjack became done, he would explode a ton or so of dynamite under it, and away up in the air the big cake would sail until it was almost out of sight. By putting a few more sticks under one side than under the other, he made sure that it would turn over while in the air, and so nicely did he calculate the exact amount of explosive to use each time that when the flapjack came down again it landed exactly on the griddle with the brown side uppermost.

After this, Paul's men never had any cause for kicking about the flapjacks in the Red River Camp, except occasionally when a cook-boy was caught by the batter and served up in the hot cake—which usually didn't happen more than two or three times a month.

THE RED RIVER CAMP

The great flapjack griddle was not the only noteworthy feature of Paul's Red River Camp, however, nor did his men dine exclusively upon flapjacks—as one might perhaps think they did from the attention given that particular item of the menu. Indeed, other foods made up most of every meal, the flapjacks being merely served for dessert, and the kitchen of the great cook shanty where most of the dishes were prepared was so big that the hundreds of cooks and all their helpers could work in it and never get in one another's way. Like everything else in any of Paul Bunyan's camps, the cooking was well organized, and each person in all the army of cooks, first and second assistant cooks, fire-tenders, pot-rustlers, butchers and dishwashers had his own particular work to do, and did it in the quickest and best way possible.

There were the men who drove the salt and pepper wagons, going down the full length of one of the big dinner tables in the dining hall the first half of the week, filling the salt and pepper shakers, and coming back the last half. The teamster that drove the catsup wagon, though, always ran out of catsup before he got halfway through with his trip, and so finally one day he became disgusted with such a job and dumped his wagon with its load into the river. The catsup colored the water, which is red to this day, thus giving to the stream the name of Red River which it still bears.

The mess hall in the Red River Camp was so large that Paul had to have lunch counters along the sides so that his men could stop and get something to eat while finding their places at the tables, or else they would get faint for want of food in looking for them. Under the huge beams of the roof, the tables and benches stood in rank after rank, as far as the eye could see, like an army on parade.

The cooks always had to use field glasses when they wanted to see how the men were getting along with any special dish being served.

Such wonderful food was served in Paul's camp that even the mice benefited from it. Just from picking up the

crumbs that fell from the tables to the floor, they soon grew so big that they ran all the wolves out of the country, and the settlers that came into the Dakotas later on shot them for tigers.

This mess hall being so big, there was some trouble at first in getting the food to the tables while it was still hot, so Paul—who was always eager to try out new ideas—began to think out some way of giving quicker service. At first he tried using ponies on roller skates to carry the food to his men, and wonderful speed they made, but as they quite often spilled their loads when turning corners he had to give them up and try some other plan.

He finally built tracks between the rows of tables and put in freight trains with specially built cars for carrying the food, and got rid of the ponies. The new plan was successful, except that there was some trouble in getting the soup to the tables without sloshing it out. This difficulty was done away with finally by serving the soup direct from the boilers where it was made, using six-inch fire hose for the purpose and fixing a big soup spigot to serve every five men.

There's no doubt about it, Paul's crews ate a tremendous amount of food, and for a long time all the supplies were carried to the camp by Babe. Once, on one of these trips with food for the camp, Paul got a little careless with Babe. The Great Blue Ox was carrying a load of split peas (this being shortly after Paul had invented the split pea so that his cooks could make twice as much soup out of a load of peas) and his master, thinking of something else and not paying close attention to what he was doing, led the heavily

laden animal across a lake where the ice was only six feet thick. Babe, of course, broke through the thin ice and spilled the entire load of peas into the lake.

Paul was accordingly greatly worried for a little while over the prospect of his men having to go for several weeks without their pea soup, but he didn't stay worried long. He just called out the Seven Axmen and the Big Swede, and some of his other good men and put them all under the leadership of Hot Biscuit Slim, the boss cook. They worked around until they pried up the lake enough so that they could build a big fire under it, and they made the peas into soup then and there, later pumping it to the cook shanty through a big fire hose. Thus Paul came through the accident without any loss, and the men liked that soup the best of all because of the fish from the lake that were cooked in it.

PAUL BUNYAN'S LAST EXPLOITS

It was Paul Bunyan who invented the Round Turn, which is still in use, no better one ever having been devised. Turning the Great Blue Ox about had always been a lot of trouble, as Paul had always done it simply by picking up Babe and setting him down again headed in the other direction. He got tired of doing this so many times every day, and at last he figured out a new method. He taught Babe to walk in a small half-circle so that when he stopped he was headed back in the opposite direction. This was the Round Turn, whereby an animal or team turns *itself* around instead of being lifted around and it was such a sensible way that it is still in use. Nowadays, very few people follow Paul's old method of turning their work animals about.

After Paul Bunyan had started using the Mississippi River for floating his logs to the mills, he one time made a mistake. He had received an order for a drive of logs from a big sawmill down near the mouth of the river, below New Orleans. The logs were made into a big raft, and Paul sent a crew of his men along to deliver it to the mill. When they reached their destination, they found the mill owner had changed his mind, and that he refused to accept the logs unless the price was made much lower than had been agreed. He, of course, thought that nothing else could be done except to take what he offered, since the logs were where they were and it would be almost impossible to get them upstream again.

Paul was not the man to be cheated in this way, however, and as soon as he received this message from his men he determined to get the logs back and fool the rascally mill owner. He thought over the matter for a while, and then went out to where the Great Blue Ox, Babe, and his mate Bessie, the Yaller Cow, were feeding. He gave each of them a hogshead or two of salt, which they gulped down greedily, and then he led them away to the upper waters of the river. The salt which they had swallowed made the two animals very thirsty indeed, and by the time they reached the banks of the Mississippi they were eager for a long drink. Paul grinned as he turned them loose and let them begin to quench their thirst.

They stood out in the water and drank and drank and

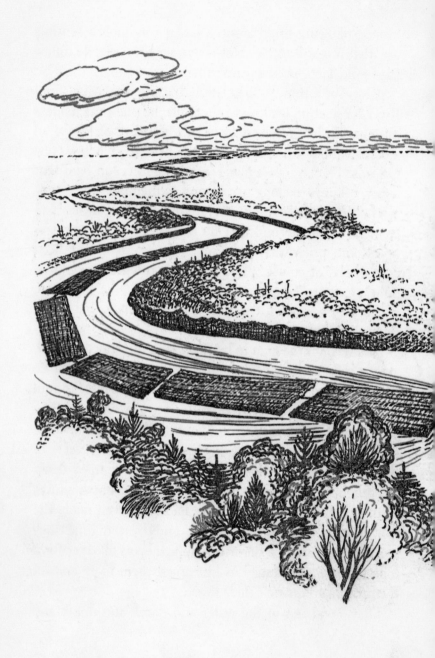

drank, and so much did they swallow and so fast did they suck up the water that the current of the river began flowing back upstream to where they were. They kept on drinking faster than ever, so thirsty were they, and together the Great Blue Ox and the Yaller Cow drank so much that finally the big log raft floated back upstream on the current that ran backwards up the river. Thus Paul got back his logs and nothing was lost by the transaction excepting a few hogsheads of salt.

All during the later years of his lumbering, Paul Bunyan had owned a fine farm. Here, during the summer, he would reward Babe and Bessie and his other animals by turning them out in his rich pastures.

Then something happened that made Paul give up his farm. Most of the corn he had raised that year was pop-corn. One day, after it was all harvested and put in the granary, the building accidentally caught fire and popped all the corn stored there. The flying white grains flew all over the farm until they covered the ground three or four feet deep, or perhaps even more. It didn't seem to hurt Babe, but the mule team, Jerry and Jinny, and Bessie, the Yaller Cow, thought they were having an extraordinarily severe snow blizzard and froze to death. Elmer, Paul's wonderful fore-and-aft Moose Terrier, was in the house while the popping was going on, and so he was saved.

So Babe continued to do all the hauling alone after that, until several years later, when suddenly he began to lose all of his old-time energy and interest in his tremendous tasks. His appetite also failed, and he showed in other ways that old age was upon him. This was not surprising, for the huge animal was more than a hundred years old, and had been constantly doing the heaviest kind of labor ever since he was a calf.

Paul saw to it that the Great Blue Ox was given the very best of attention, but all efforts were unavailing toward saving his life. After his death his ribs were used, so some stories tell us, to form the sides of a big locomotive roundhouse in Seattle. Paul would hardly have allowed the remains of his devoted pet to come to so sordid an end, however, and the story that says that the Olympian Mountains are the burial mound of Babe is probably the correct one.

Not long after this Mrs. Paul also passed away. The big logger mourned his double loss greatly, and it seemed from that time on he began to lose his interest in the things he used to do with so much energy and ambition. He had already begun to get very much disgusted over some of the newfangled methods which were being introduced into the woods, replacing some of the better old-fashioned ideas about logging which he had developed. So it wasn't very

long before he began to get rid of all his business interests and at last retired from all further lumbering activity.

Having too many people around always irritated Paul, except when he was in a logging camp and the people about him were his own men. Now, even the woods were beginning to get crowded, for many lumbermen were starting operations in the western forests as well as among those still standing further east, and Paul felt that his place was taken by others. With so many trying to do the work which he had done alone and on such a big scale in the olden days, his services were no longer needed.

Taking only his fore-and-aft Moose Terrier, Elmer, and his guns with him, Paul Bunyan one night slipped away from all men who knew him and went far through the thickest woods. There, in the heart of the wildest country that he could find, he put up his shanty, and there he still lives, all alone except for his dog. Men say that he can never die until the last tree is cut down, and that until such a time comes, Paul Bunyan and his lone companion will continue to roam the forests.

Once in a while he and Elmer may appear almost any place where there are trees, but as they are always going at a furious pace, it takes sharp eyes to see them at all. They are always running at great speed, chasing down the wild game that is their food. And often, when the winter winds blow harshly, whistling through the trees and moaning down chimneys and around the corners of houses, woodsmen say that these sounds are made by Paul Bunyan calling to his dog as they rush along on their endless hunting.

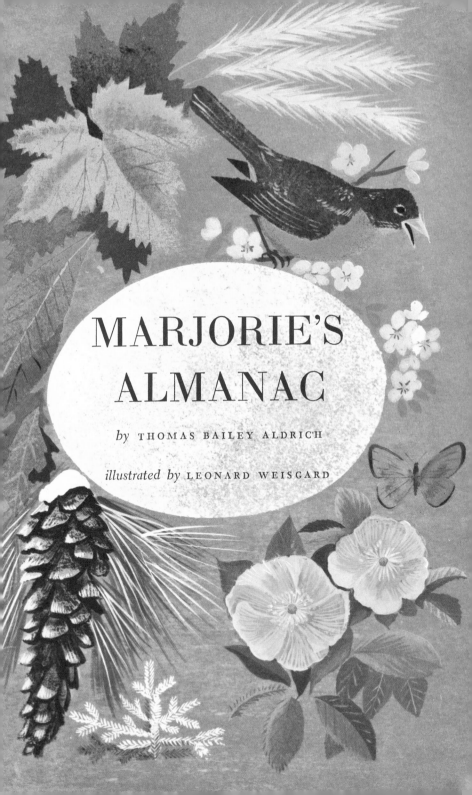

MARJORIE'S ALMANAC

by THOMAS BAILEY ALDRICH

illustrated by LEONARD WEISGARD

Robins in the treetop,
  Blossoms in the grass,
Green things a-growing
  Everywhere you pass;
Sudden little breezes,
  Showers of silver dew,
Black bough and bent twig
  Budding out anew;
Pine tree and willow tree,
  Fringèd elm and larch—
Don't you think that Maytime's
  Pleasanter than March?

Apples in the orchard
    Mellowing one by one;
Strawberries upturning
    Soft cheeks to the sun;
Roses faint with sweetness,
    Lilies fair of face,
Drowsy scents and murmurs
    Haunting every place;
Lengths of golden sunshine,
    Moonlight bright as day—
Don't you think that summer's
    Pleasanter than May?

Roger in the corn patch
    Whistling Negro songs;
Pussy by the hearthside
    Romping with the tongs;
Chestnuts in the ashes
    Bursting through the rind;
Red leaf and gold leaf
    Rustling down the wind;
Mother "doin' peaches"
    All the afternoon—
Don't you think that autumn's
    Pleasanter than June?

Little fairy snowflakes
    Dancing in the flue;
Old Mr. Santa Claus,
    What is keeping you?
Twilight and firelight
    Shadows come and go;
Merry chime of sleighbells
    Tinkling through the snow;
Mother knitting stockings
    (Pussy's got the ball) —
Don't you think that winter's
    Pleasanter than all?

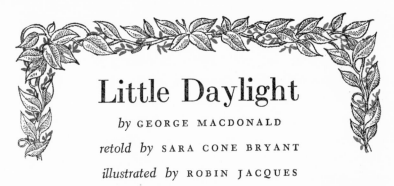

Little Daylight

by GEORGE MACDONALD

retold by SARA CONE BRYANT

illustrated by ROBIN JACQUES

Once there was a beautiful palace, which had a great wood at one side. The king and his courtiers hunted in the wood near the palace, and there it was kept open, free from underbrush. But farther away it grew wilder and wilder, till at last it was so thick that nobody knew what was there. It was a very great wood indeed.

In the wood lived eight fairies. Seven of them were good fairies, who had lived there always; the eighth was a bad fairy, who had just come. And the worst of it was that nobody but the other fairies knew she *was* a fairy; people thought she was just an ugly old witch. The good fairies lived in the dearest little houses! One lived in a hollow silver birch, one in a little moss cottage, and so on. But the bad fairy lived in a horrid mud house in the middle of a dark swamp.

Now when the first baby was born to the king and queen, her father and mother decided to name her "Daylight", because she was so bright and sweet. And of course they had a christening party. And of *course* they invited the fairies, because the good fairies had always been at the

Text from *How to Tell Stories to Children*, copyright, 1905, by Houghton Mifflin and Company, and copyright, 1933, by Sara Cone Bryant Borst.

christening party when a princess was born in the palace, and everybody knew that they brought good gifts.

But, alas, no one knew about the swamp fairy, and she was not invited—which really pleased her, because it gave her an excuse for doing something mean.

The good fairies came to the christening party, and, one after another, five of them gave little Daylight good gifts. The other two stood among the guests, so that no one noticed them. The swamp fairy thought there were no more of them; so she stepped forward, just as the archbishop was handing the baby back to the lady-in-waiting.

"I am just a little deaf," she said, mumbling a laugh with her toothless gums. "Will your reverence tell me the baby's name again?"

"Certainly, my good woman," said the bishop. "The infant is little Daylight."

"And little Daylight it shall be, forsooth," cried the bad fairy. "I decree that she shall sleep all day." Then she laughed a horrid shrieking laugh, "He, he, hi, hi!"

Everyone looked at everyone else in despair, but out stepped the sixth good fairy, who had been kept back to undo what she could of what the swamp fairy might decree.

"Then at least she shall wake all night," she said, sadly.

"Ah!" screamed the swamp fairy, "you spoke before I had finished, which is against the law, and gives me another chance." All the fairies started at once to say, "I beg your pardon!" But the bad fairy said, "I had only laughed 'he, he!' and 'hi, hi!' I had still 'ho, ho!' and 'hu, hu!' to laugh."

The fairies could not say anything, and the bad fairy

had her other chance. She said:

"Since she is to wake all night, I decree that she shall wax and wane with the moon! Ho, ho, hu, hu!"

Out stepped the last good fairy. "Until a prince shall kiss her without knowing who she is," she said, quickly.

The swamp fairy had been prepared for the trick of keeping back one good fairy, but she had not suspected two, and she could not say a word, for she had laughed "ho, ho!" and "hu, hu!"

The poor king and queen looked sad enough. "We don't know what you mean," they said to the good fairy who had spoken last. But the good fairy only smiled. "The meaning of the thing will come with the thing," she said.

That was the end of the party, but it was only the beginning of the trouble. Can you imagine what a queer household it would be, where the baby laughed and crowed all night, and slept all day? Little Daylight was as merry and bright all night as any baby in the world, but with the first sign of dawn she fell asleep, and slept like a little dormouse till dark. Nothing could waken her while day lasted. Still, the royal family did get used to this; but the rest of the bad fairy's gift was a great deal worse—that about waxing and waning with the moon. You know how the moon grows bigger and brighter each night, from the time it is a curly silver thread low in the sky till it is round and golden, flooding the whole sky with light? That is the waxing moon. Then, you know, it wanes; it grows smaller and paler again, night by night, till at last it disappears for awhile, altogether. Well, poor little Daylight waxed and waned with it. She was the rosiest, plumpest, merriest baby in the world when the moon was at the full; but as it began to wane her little cheeks grew paler, her tiny hands thinner, with every night, till she lay in her cradle like a shadow-baby, without sound or motion. At first they thought she was dead, when the moon disappeared, but after some months they got used to this too, and only waited eagerly for the new moon, to see her revive. When it shone again, faint and silver on the horizon, the baby stirred weakly, and then they fed her gently. Each night she grew a little better, and when the moon was near the full again, she was again a lively, rosy, lovely child.

So it went on till she grew up. She grew to be the most beautiful maiden the moon ever shone on, and everyone loved her so much, for her sweet ways and her merry heart, that someone was always planning to stay up at night, to be near her. But she did not like to be watched, especially when she felt the bad time of waning coming on; so her ladies-in-waiting had to be very careful. When the moon waned she became shrunken and pale and bent, like an old, old woman, worn out with sorrow. Only her golden hair and her blue eyes remained unchanged, and this gave her a terribly strange look. At last, as the moon disappeared, she faded away to a little, bowed, old creature, asleep and helpless.

No wonder she liked best to be alone! She got in the way of wandering by herself in the beautiful wood, playing in the moonlight when she was well, stealing away in the shadows when she was fading with the moon. Her father had a lovely little house of roses and vines built for her there. It stood at the edge of a most beautiful open glade,

inside the wood, where the moon shone best. There the
princess lived with her ladies. And there she danced when
the moon waned; her ladies often lost her altogether, so

far did she wander. And sometimes they found her sleeping under a great tree, and brought her home in their arms.

When the princess was about seventeen years old, there was a rebellion in a kingdom not far from her father's. Wicked nobles murdered the king of the country and would have murdered the young prince, too, if he had not escaped, dressed in peasant's clothes.

Dressed in his poor rags, the prince wandered about a long time, till one day he got into a great wood, and lost his way. It was the wood where the Princess Daylight lived, but of course he did not know anything about that nor about her. He wandered till night, and then he came to a queer little house. One of the good fairies lived there, and the minute she saw him she knew all about everything; but to him she looked only like a kind old woman. She gave him a good supper and a bed for the night, and told him to come back to her if he found no better place for the next night. But the prince said he must get out of the wood at once; so in the morning he took leave of the fairy.

All day long he walked, and walked; but at nightfall he had not found his way out of the wood, so he lay down to rest till the moon should rise and light his path.

When he woke the moon was glorious; it was three days from the full, and bright as silver. By its light he saw what he thought to be the edge of the wood, and he hastened toward it. But when he came to it, it was only an open space, surrounded with trees. It was so very lovely, in the white moonlight, that the prince stood a minute to look. And as he looked, something white moved out of the trees on the far side of the open space. It was something slim and

white, that swayed in the dim light like a young birch.

"It must be a moon fairy," thought the prince; and he stepped into the shadow.

The moon fairy came nearer and nearer, dancing and swaying in the moonlight. And as she came, she began to sing a soft, gay little song.

But when she was quite close, the prince saw that she was not a fairy after all, but a real human maiden, the loveliest maiden he had ever seen. Her hair was like yellow corn, and her smile made all the place merry. Her white gown fluttered as she danced, and her little song sounded like a bird note.

The prince watched her till she danced out of sight, and then until she once more came toward him. And she seemed so like a moonbeam herself, as she lifted her face to the sky, that he was almost afraid to breathe. He had never seen anything so lovely. By the time she had danced twice round the circle, he could think of nothing in the world except the hope of finding out who she was, and staying near her.

But while he was waiting for her to appear the third time, his weariness overcame him, and he fell asleep. And when he awoke, it was broad day, and the beautiful maiden had vanished.

He hunted about, hoping to find where she lived, and on the other side of the glade he came upon a lovely little house, covered with moss and climbing roses. He thought she must live there, so he went round to the kitchen door and asked the kind cook for a drink of water, and while he was drinking it he asked who lived there. She told him it was the house of the Princess Daylight, but she told him nothing else about her, because she was not allowed to talk about her mistress. But she gave him a very good meal and told him other things.

He did not go back to the little old woman who had been so kind to him first, but wandered all day in the wood, waiting for the moon-time. Again he waited at the edge of the dell, and when the white moon was high in the heavens, once more he saw the glimmering in the distance, and once more the lovely maiden floated toward him. He knew her name was the Princess Daylight, but this time she seemed to him much lovelier than before. She was all in blue like the blue of the sky in summer. (She really was more lovely, you know, because the moon was almost at the full.) All night he watched her, quite forgetting that he ought not to be doing it, till she disappeared on the opposite side of the glade. Then, very tired, he found his way to the little old woman's house, had breakfast with her, and fell fast asleep in the bed she gave him.

The fairy knew well enough by his face that he had seen Daylight, and when he woke up in the evening and started off again she gave him a strange little flask and told him to use it if ever he needed it.

This night the princess did not appear in the dell until midnight, at the very full of the moon. But when she came, she was so lovely that she took the prince's breath away. Just think!—she was dressed in a gown that looked as if it were made of fireflies' wings, embroidered in gold. She danced around and around, singing, swaying, and flitting like a beam of sunlight, till the prince grew quite dazzled.

But while he had been watching her, he had not noticed that the sky was growing dark and the wind was rising. Suddenly there was a clap of thunder. The princess danced on. But another clap came louder, and then a sudden great flash of lightning that lit up the sky from end to end. The prince couldn't help shutting his eyes, but he opened them quickly to see if Daylight was hurt. Alas, she was lying on the ground. The prince ran to her, but she was already up again.

"Who are you?" she said.

"I thought," stammered the prince, "you might be hurt."

"There is nothing the matter. Go away."

The prince went sadly.

"Come back," said the princess. The prince came. "I like you, you do as you are told. Are you good?"

"Not so good as I should like to be," said the prince.

"Then go and grow better," said the princess.

The prince went, more sadly.

"Come back," said the princess. The prince came. "I think you must be a prince," she said.

"Why?" said the prince.

"Because you do as you are told, and you tell the truth. Will you tell me what the sun looks like?"

"Why, everybody knows that," said the prince.

"I am different from everybody," said the princess, "I don't know."

"But," said the prince, "do you not look when you wake up in the morning?"

"That's just it," said the princess, "I never do wake up in the morning. I never can wake up until——" Then the princess remembered that she was talking to a prince, and putting her hands over her face she walked swiftly away. The prince followed her, but she turned and put up her hand to tell him not to. And like the gentleman prince that he was, he obeyed her at once.

Now all this time, the wicked swamp fairy had not known a word about what was going on. But now she found out, and she was furious, for fear that little Daylight should be delivered from her spell. So she cast her spells to keep the prince from finding Daylight again. Night after night the poor prince wandered and wandered, and never could find the little dell. And when it came daytime, of course there was no princess to be seen. Finally, at the time that the moon was almost gone, the swamp fairy stopped making spells, because she knew that by this time

Daylight would be so changed and ugly that the prince would never know her if he did see her. She said to herself with a wicked laugh, "No fear of his wanting to kiss her now!"

That night the prince did find the dell, but no princess came. A little after midnight he passed near the lovely little house where she lived, and there he overheard her waiting women talking about her. They seemed in great distress. They were saying that the princess had wandered into the woods and was lost. The prince didn't know, of

course, what it meant, but he did understand that the princess was lost somewhere, and he started off to find her. After he had gone a long way without finding her, he came to a big old tree, and there he thought he would light a fire to show her the way if she should happen to see it.

As the blaze flared up, he suddenly saw a little black heap on the other side of the tree. Somebody was lying there. He ran to the spot, his heart beating with hope. But when he lifted the cloak which was huddled about the form, he saw at once that it was not Daylight. A pinched, withered,

59

white, little old woman's face shone out at him. The hood was drawn close down over her forehead, the eyes were closed, and as the prince lifted the cloak, the old woman's lips moaned faintly.

"Oh, poor mother," said the prince, "what is the matter?" The old woman only moaned again. The prince lifted her and carried her over to the warm fire, and rubbed her hands, trying to find out what was the matter. But she only moaned, and her face was so terribly strange and white that the prince's tender heart ached for her. Remembering his little flask, he poured some of its liquid between her lips, and then he thought the best thing he could do was to carry her to the princess's house, where she could be taken care of.

As he lifted the poor little form in his arms, two great tears stole out from the old woman's closed eyes and ran down her wrinkled cheeks.

"Oh, poor, poor mother," said the prince pityingly; and he stooped and kissed her withered lips.

As he walked through the forest with the old woman in his arms, it seemed to him that she grew heavier and heavier; he could hardly carry her at all. And then she stirred, and at last he was obliged to set her down, to rest. He meant to lay her on the ground. But the old woman stood up on her feet.

And then her hood fell back from her face. As she looked up at the prince, the first, long, yellow ray of the rising sun struck full upon her—and it was the Princess Daylight! Her hair was golden as the sun itself, and her eyes as blue as the flower that grows in the corn.

The prince fell on his knees before her. But she gave him her hand and made him rise.

"You kissed me when I was an old woman," said the princess, "I'll kiss you now that I am a young princess." And she did.

And then she turned her face toward the dawn.

"Dear Prince," she said, "is that the sun?"

Kiki Skates

written and illustrated by CHARLOTTE STEINER

Kiki was spending winter vacation with her grandmother in the country. How surprised she was the first day!

The country looked different in the winter. There were no green leaves on the trees. And no green grassy fields to play in.

But the next morning Kiki was even more surprised. The fields were covered with snow. The roads were covered with snow. Even the trees looked white.

Kiki hurried to put on her snow suit.

But the snow was so deep she could hardly open the door. Grandmother gave her a new shovel. It was fun to dig a path to the road.

But the snow was too deep on the road. Kiki could hardly walk.

She tried snowshoes. But she couldn't walk very well in those, either.

The next morning the big snowplow cleared the road.

Kiki ran down the road to see her friend Ellen. Ellen was waiting for Kiki. Ellen had a sled.

That was fun. All morning Kiki and Ellen and the other boys and girls coasted down the hill near Ellen's house.

On their way home they met Johnny. He was carrying two

66

long boards over his shoulders.
"What are those?" Kiki asked.

"Skis, of course," he said. "See how fast I can go." He
strapped on his skis and glided over the crusty snow.

The next day Johnny brought Kiki his little sister's skis. Skiing looked easy, but it wasn't. Kiki's legs wouldn't go straight ahead as Johnny's did. One leg went to the right, the other to the left, and there was Kiki in the middle of the snow.

Getting up was hard too. Johnny showed Kiki how to straighten her skis and stand up.

He showed her how to climb a hill without slipping. And how to stop without falling.

Kiki was tired when she got home. And very hungry too.

It was so cold the next day that the pond was frozen hard.
All the children were skating but Kiki did not have skates,
so Ellen pushed her on a funny little chair with runners.
That was fun. But not as much fun as skating, Kiki thought.

So that night Kiki wrote a letter.

Dear Mommy,
Please tell Santa I want skates for Christmas most of all.

And the day after that Kiki and Ellen built a snow family.

And they went for a ride in an old-fashioned sleigh. That was fun—but not as much fun as skating, Kiki said.

After Kiki went back home to town, she missed the snow. But Christmas was coming. And under the tree she found a very exciting box. In it there was a pretty flared skirt, a sweater with her name on it, a cap with a tassel, and best of all SKATES!!!

She tried them on right away. And walked on the rug.

Skating was easy, Kiki thought.

But the next day at the ice rink, Kiki's skates were as hard to manage as the skis. Poor Kiki couldn't stand up.

Then one of the instructors took Kiki's hand. He showed
her how to balance and how to glide.

Kiki had a wonderful time. She could hardly wait to get home. "Oh, Daddy," she called, "I can skate. I only fell down twice."

The
Three Billy Goats
Gruff

illustrated by FEODOR ROJANKOVSKY

Once upon a time there were three Billy Goats. They
lived in a meadow on a hillside, and the name of all three
Billy Goats was "Gruff".

The meadow where they lived had very little grass in it, and the Billy Goats were hungry. They wanted to go up the hillside to a fine meadow full of grass and daisies, where they could eat and get fat. But on the way up there was a bridge over a burn, and under the bridge lived a great ugly Troll, who was as horrid as he was ugly.

So first of all came the youngest Billy Goat Gruff to cross the bridge.

"TRIP, TRAP! TRIP, TRAP!" went the bridge.

"WHO'S THAT tripping over my bridge?" roared the Troll.

"Oh, it's only I, the tiniest Billy Goat Gruff, and I'm

going up the hillside to make myself fat," said the Billy
Goat, who had a very small voice.

"No you're not," said the Troll, "for I'm coming to
gobble you up!"

"Oh! Please don't take me. I'm too little, that I am,"
said the Billy Goat. "Wait till the second Billy Goat Gruff
comes; he's much bigger."

"Well then, be off with you," said the Troll.

A little later came the second Billy Goat Gruff to cross the bridge.

"TRIP, TRAP! TRIP, TRAP! TRIP, TRAP!" went the bridge.

"WHO'S THAT tripping over my bridge?" roared the Troll.

"Oh, it's only I, the second Billy Goat Gruff, and I'm

going up the hillside to make myself fat," said the Billy Goat, who hadn't such a very small voice.

"No you're not," said the Troll, "for I'm coming to gobble you up!"

"Oh, please don't take me. Wait a little, till the big Billy Goat Gruff comes; he's much bigger."

"Very well, be off with you," said the Troll.

But just then, up came the big Billy Goat Gruff.

"TRIP, TRAP! TRIP, TRAP! TRIP, TRAP! TRIP, TRAP!" went the bridge; for the Billy Goat was so heavy that the bridge creaked and groaned under him.

"WHO'S THAT tramping over my bridge?" roared the Troll.

"IT IS I, THE BIG BILLY GOAT GRUFF," said the Billy Goat, who had a great loud voice.

82

"NOW—I'm coming to gobble you up!" roared the Troll.

"Well, come along!" said the big Billy Goat Gruff. "I've got two horns and four hard hoofs. See what you can do!"

That was what the big Billy Goat Gruff said. So along came the Troll, and the big Billy Goat Gruff flew at that ugly, great Troll, and he spiked him with his horns, and he trampled him with his hard hoofs, and he tossed him over the bridge into the burn. Then the big Billy Goat Gruff went up the hillside.

There the three Billy Goats Gruff got so fat that they couldn't walk home again. And if they couldn't walk home, they are there yet.

> So *snip, snap, snout,*
> *This tale's told out.*

Tell Me the Time, Please

by LILLIAN J. BRAGDON

illustrated by

LEONARD KESSLER

"Wake up, Sleepy Head!" Mr. Sun seems to say as he peeps in your window. "Here's a new day!"

"Ting-a-ling-ling!" rings the alarm clock in your mother's room. "It's time to get up."

The rising sun is Nature's way of telling time, and the clock is man's way.

The story of how men learned to measure time is a long and interesting one. It will take you to many far countries.

When you were very little, though there were clocks in your house, you were too young to tell time by them.

Your mother told you when it was time for breakfast, time to go out to play, time for lunch, time for supper. But all *you* knew was DAYTIME when it was light, and NIGHTTIME when darkness came after the sun went down. Then, tired from play, you snuggled once more under the blankets.

Just so did the Cave Man divide TIME—by light and darkness. He had no clock or any way to tell time except by the Sun. As he watched it travel slowly across the sky, he could almost hear Mr. Sun saying, "Hunt your bear, catch your fish and gather wood for your fires. Night and darkness will soon drive me away. Then you must be safe in your cave. Hurry! Hurry!"

Indians lived out-of-doors, like the Cave Men, and they, too, had no clocks.

When nighttime came, the Indian Chief and his warriors gathered round the campfire. They told of the wonderful things they had seen and heard as they hunted the deer or laid traps for the black bear among the rocks on the mountainside.

An Indian father, telling stories to his son, did not begin them, "Once upon a time," as we often do, but said, "Many moons ago." The Indians looked to the sky to measure time. They said, "After three moons," or "When the new moon is in the sky."

Tonight, if the sky is clear, look up at the stars and pick out the brightest one you can find. Suppose you said to

your mother, "When that star is over the church steeple, I will go to bed." It might take hours and hours for the star to travel that distance. Only a person who has watched and studied the stars knows how to tell time by them.

In faraway Babylon, thousands of years ago, men told time by the stars. Night after night, the old priests, who were the wise men, studied the skies and watched the stars. They gave them names and made up stories about them.

Do you remember the little boy in the poem who had "a little shadow" that went "in and out" with him? And the shadow was short if the sun was high, and long if it was low?

Well, thousands of years ago, in faraway Egypt, men first began to watch shadows, and used them to tell time.

They noticed that at a certain time the shadow of the pyramid was very long on the sand of the desert. Later the shadow had grown shorter. They learned to tell just what time of day it was by the length of the shadow.

But men could not very well run to the pyramid whenever they wanted to know the time. Some other way had to

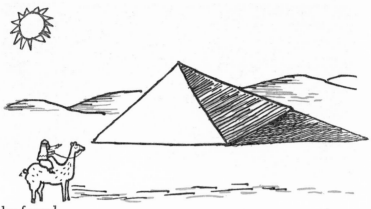

be found.

What do you think they did?

They planted a stick in the ground and measured time by its changing shadow. They found that the shadow of the stick moved in the same way the shadow of the pyramid had moved. Now anyone could tell the time if he had a SHADOW STICK, as the strange clock was called.

In a sunny spot in Grandmother's garden, stands another kind of old shadow clock known as the SUNDIAL. The metal part that stands upright on a stone base casts a

shadow on the flat face. This face is divided into hours, as on our clocks.

Today we use sundials to add beauty to our gardens, but long ago they were the only clocks some people had.

But when the rain and storms came, clocks that told time by measuring the sun's shadow were of no use. So the old priests found a new way to tell time. They twisted dry grass into a rope, tying knots at equal distances. Then they set fire to one end and measured the time it took to burn from knot to knot.

Even today, in some parts of Korea, time is measured by the knotted rope.

About five thousand years ago the Chinese measured time with a WATER CLOCK. A very simple one was a bowl with a tiny hole in the bottom of it. This was placed in a pan of water, and as the bowl filled, it sank. Then the man who was watching it struck a bell to let the people know an hour had passed.

In England, good King Alfred measured time with the CANDLE CLOCK. He made a twelve-inch candle in

bands of black and white. Each band was one inch wide and took twenty minutes to burn, so the whole candle took four hours. Six candles were burned in the twenty-four hours of a day and a night.

The old monk in the picture cut a notch in a stick each time a band of the candle clock was burned. In this way he kept a record of the passing hours, and knew when to ring the church bells to tell people it was time to come to church, or to cover their fires and go to bed. Church bells were the only timekeepers that some people had in those olden days.

When the Pilgrims first came to America, they brought with them a sand clock, known as the HOURGLASS. No

one knows who first used this clock but it is very old.

This picture will show you how the hourglass looked and how it worked. It took one hour for the sand to flow from one bowl to the other.

In Colonial days ministers preached long sermons. Little boys and girls grew very tired sitting still so long. They watched the hourglass hoping that when the top half was empty, the minister would stop talking.

But sometimes he turned it over again and went right on. When that happened it was almost more than they could bear. Don't you feel sorry for them?

Most of the timekeepers you have read about so far were not very exact.

People in the olden days did not need to hurry, so it did not matter whether their time was quite right or not.

Today you must not be even one minute late to school.

As men began to have more things to do, they had to find a better way of measuring time.

We do not know who made the first clock that told time by hands moving around its face. We do know that clocks that worked with heavy weights, and wheels with teeth around their edges, began to appear on public buildings and churches about 1300.

The weights turned the wheels that made the clocks run.

About three hundred and fifty years later a pendulum was used to make clocks keep better time. When the clock went too fast, the pendulum was made longer, but it was shortened if the clock was slow. At first the pendulum swung back and forth across the face, but later it was placed at the back of the clock.

The first house clock with wheels and a pendulum was made in the shape of a lantern and so was known as a LANTERN CLOCK.

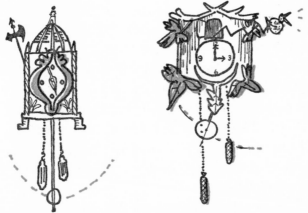

Because of the pendulum that hung below the face, it had to be fastened to the wall.

Another pendulum clock which we still use today and which boys and girls love to listen to is the CUCKOO CLOCK.

At each hour a little bird appears at a door near the top of the clock, and tells the hour by the number of his cheerful cuckoos.

This clock is usually built like a little rustic house or a Swiss chalet, and runs by weights.

THE GRANDFATHER CLOCKS were often more than six feet tall. The long pendulums and weights were hidden inside beautiful oak or mahogany cases. Many of them had a set of chimes which struck the hours.

Some of these grandfather clocks, that still keep perfect time, told time for the men who fought in the Revolutionary War.

Of course, all old-fashioned clocks had to be wound to make them go. Some clocks were wound every day and some only once a week.

Every Saturday night Grandfather would go from room to room winding all the clocks.

The first WATCH, made of iron, and shaped like an egg, was made about 1500, in a quaint old town in Germany. It was very heavy. Until this watch was made, men carried small sundials and hourglasses in their pockets.

Watches were called pocket clocks.

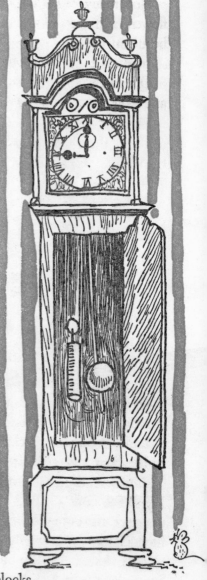

Not many years later, watches shaped like animals, flowers and insects were made. They were covered with beautiful jewels.

In France, watchmakers were called Toy-men.

Queen Elizabeth chose her watches to match her dresses and wore them on a chain or ribbon.

When watches had to be made by hand, only the very rich could own them.

Some of the finest watches are still made in Geneva, Switzerland.

Nowadays, our factories turn them out so quickly and cheaply, that most boys and girls can have a watch as soon as they learn to tell time.

Our great-great-grandfathers had heavy gold RE-PEATER WATCHES which could strike the hours, quarters, and even minutes. They were used to tell the time in the dark. They were very expensive. Nowadays a much cheaper watch is made, with the figures and hands that can be seen in the dark.

Time went on. Men learned about electricity. They learned how to make it work for them. Today, electric current runs many of the clocks in our homes, schools, factories, and public buildings.

The early settlers of Connecticut, who laughed at Eli Terry as he peddled his homemade wooden clocks from door to door, would be surprised to see the large clock factories for which Connecticut is now famous.

The New England States lead this country in the making of clocks.

Radio and television, though not clocks, are "the voice of time." Frequent announcements of the hour are made on all stations.

When you hear the announcer say, "It is exactly fifteen minutes past eight o'clock," you know how soon it will be time to start for school.

Sailors, on board ship, have a way of their own of telling time. With them, time is divided by bells. Thus: at noon, at four, and at eight o'clock, eight bells announce the hour. Half past twelve, half past four, and half past eight are announced by one bell. For each half hour after that, one extra bell is added, until we come again to twelve and four and eight o'clock.

Many people in America have heard Big Ben in London chime the hour of midnight over the radio on New Year's Eve. Big Ben, one of the oldest and best known clocks in the world, is on Westminster Clock Tower. It has four dials, each one twenty-three feet across. The big bell is so heavy that it has twice cracked.

Far up above the rushing crowds, Big Ben marks the

passing of time.

When you go to Europe, you may visit the Strasbourg Cathedral. Inside it, under a beautiful stained glass window, is a most interesting clock. It is shaped like a smaller cathedral and has three dials. One is a calendar, one a clock, and one shows the position of the moon and stars.

There are little figures that pass along a gallery as the chimes strike the hour. At noon a cock, perched on the top of the tower, flaps his wings and crows *cock-a-doodle-do*.

The Colgate Clock in Jersey City is the largest clock in the world. Because of the heavy winds off the Hudson River, the framework of a dial is used instead of a solid face. This skeleton dial is thirty-eight feet across.

At night the hands and minute marks are outlined in white lights. Red lights mark the five-minute divisions.

To measure time around the world we say that day begins in Greenwich, England. Suppose you were at Greenwich at daybreak and could take a big jump westward across the Atlantic Ocean. You would find New York still in darkness. It would take about five hours for the earth to turn enough so that daybreak began to appear in New York.

If you are in New York and hear a radio announcer at St. Louis say, "It is 9 o'clock, Central Standard Time," you are surprised to see that your watch shows 10 o'clock.

As the earth spins it takes one hour after sunrise in New York to turn enough for the sun's rays to reach St. Louis. So New York time is always one hour ahead of St. Louis time.

In the United States we have four divisions of time, each one hour apart. They are:

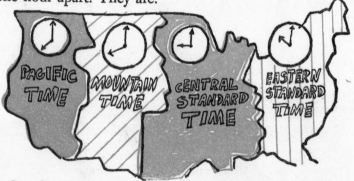

So when it is 10 o'clock in New York, it is 9 o'clock in St. Louis, 8 o'clock in Denver, and 7 o'clock in San Francisco or on the Pacific coast.

Some states and cities also use Daylight Saving Time in the summer months, during which clocks are set one hour later than usual.

At the Naval Observatory, in Washington, is the master

clock from which all other clocks in the United States are set.

The Government broadcasts Official Time from the Radio Station at Arlington, Virginia.

Men study the stars and set this official clock by them, for the stars never vary.

And so, after thousands of years, during which man has learned so much, he still looks to the stars to tell time.

There are many ways of telling Time,
To this you will agree.
An easy one is to learn by rhyme;
Just turn the page and see.

AN EASY RHYME
FOR TELLING TIME

There are twelve numbers on my face,
Five tiny marks fill in each space.
One long hand, and a short one too;
Now watch and see what they can do.

The large hand always leads the way
No matter what the time of day.
Each tiny mark one minute shows;
The large hand counts them as it goes.

On number 12 the long hand stands
The even hour to show,
When round the face it travels fast
We watch the minutes go.

When on the 12 the long hand rests
And on the 6 the small,
We say it is just 6 o'clock
And folks to supper call.

The long hand travels on to 3—
Oh dear, what is the time?
Just count the tiny marks; you'll see
Fifteen in one long line.

So with the short hand still on 6
The long one stopped on 3
It's fifteen minutes after 6.
Quite simple—don't you see?

Again the long hand travels on,
At 5 we see it rest.
We count the tiny marks once more
And this is a real test:

We start on 12 and count straight through
Till on the number 5
We find with joy that we have reached
The sum of twenty-five.

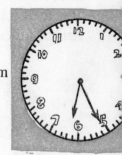

"It is twenty-five minutes past 6," we exclaim
As we look at the clock in surprise.
This telling of time is really a game
For children with bright young eyes.

The long hand moves on;
It's on 6, don't you see?
Now tell me, my children,
What time can it be?

Thirty minute-marks small
From the top to this spot
It marks just half past 6
When it's right on the dot.

This tireless hand moves to 8 you now see,
While the little hand still stays near 6.
How many marks now from the 12 back to 8
So the time of the day we may fix?

It's a full twenty marks, and the time we must say
Is twenty minutes to 7,
Because we now start at the top of the clock
And count backwards through the 11.

Once more it moves on, till it reaches the 9,
It's travelled three-quarters the way.
It is fast coming up to your bedtime and mine—
It's a quarter to 7 we say.

Just fifteen marks more and on 12 we shall be,
The long hand has travelled clear round.
We have counted the dots as we circle the face,
In an hour just sixty we've found.

Streamlined Wonder World

by DAVIS COLE

illustrated by RICHARD M. POWERS

There are dozens of wonderful streamlined trains in this country. If you started out to take a ride on each of them, you'd have to travel for weeks. One man who has already gone a hundred thousand miles in them isn't through yet.

Text from *The Real Book About Trains*, copyright, 1951, by Franklin Watts, Inc., and published by Garden City Books.

104

So let's take an imaginary trip on a special train that combines some of the interesting things found on many different streamliners.

The most fun is probably a car called a Vista-dome, built on two levels. Downstairs it's like an ordinary comfortable

coach. The upstairs section has a "blister" top—windows on all sides and on top, too. Here you sit in a seat that can be turned around in any direction. You can look up at mountain peaks. You can take photographs of everything all around. You can watch the stars at night. The chairs

downstairs in the car have backs that tip into any position you find comfortable. Folding rests slide out for your arms and legs and feet. As you go through particularly interesting country, a loudspeaker announces things to look for and tells you stories about them.

When you are hungry, you have your choice of several places to eat on a streamliner. If you want just a snack, you can go to a sort of sandwich shop in the Vista-dome car. For a big meal, you may go to a diner which is exactly like an expensive restaurant. Or, if you don't want to spend quite so much money, you go to a different diner at the other end of the train. Here the food is just as good but not quite so fancy or served in such elegant style.

After dinner, you sit for a while in the lounge-observation car and listen to the radio. Here are deep comfortable armchairs like the ones in a living room, couches too, racks of magazines, and tables arranged with straight chairs for people who want to play games.

Before you go to bed, you decide to make a telephone call. So you sit in a booth at one end of the car and pick up a regular telephone. In a short time the operator has put your call through. A radio-telephone setup on the train connects with a regular telephone office along the way. By a combination of the two, you can talk to people anywhere, while you speed along at eighty miles an hour.

Now for some sleep. If you have a regular coach ticket, you will go to your seat in the coach, tilt it back comfortably, pull out the leg rest, and stretch out for a nap. Ring for the porter, and he will bring you a pillow, too.

But suppose you have a Pullman ticket. This entitles you to a bed or berth in a sleeping car. Today there are several different kinds of sleeping cars. If you ask your mother or father how they used to travel in Pullmans, they will probably describe this kind: It has double seats which face each other and can be made into a bed called a lower berth. Above it, a kind of shelf swings down, making an upper berth. Long green curtains hang from the ceiling to the floor, and you button them on the inside

To get into the upper berth, you ask the porter for a ladder. You push a button which rings for him when you want to come down, unless you want to jump about five feet to the floor.

In some cars, each upper berth has its own little ladder that folds back out of the way when you aren't using it.

In the days when Pullman cars were new and fascinating

inventions, people felt a little shy about walking up and down the aisle in bathrobes and slippers. So it was quite a chore to sit in a berth and wriggle in or out of the bulky, complicated clothes that almost everybody wore then. Ladies had to take off and put away several sets of petticoats. Children had to wrestle with long underwear and high-buttoned shoes.

Nowadays you go to one of the dressing rooms at the end of the car, where there are washstands and toilets, chairs and mirrors, towels, and gadgets that squirt soap.

The newer Pullman cars have separate little rooms. One kind is called a duplex-roomette. The outside of this car looks peculiar, with windows arranged checkerboard fashion—one low, the next high, the next low, and so on. The reason is that the little rooms inside are staggered, too. Some are at floor level, and some are on a higher level, reached by climbing a few steps.

Maybe your ticket calls for a larger room in a different kind of car. Suppose you have a kind called a "bedroom,"

which opens off a long corridor on one side of the car. In this one you'll find a couch that can be made into a bed, with an upper berth that lets down from the ceiling.

In some Pullman cars, the walls between rooms fold back, so that two or more rooms can be made into a whole house for a family traveling together.

Some of the rooms have comfortable armchairs that push aside or fold up at night. Most rooms have washbowls and clothes closets and toilets. And some even have their own shower baths. Double panes of glass keep the windows from getting foggy in winter. And special kinds of soundproofing make the cars so quiet that you really can sleep in them.

All the cars on streamlined trains have air conditioning. Switches in the Pullman rooms allow you to keep as warm or as cool as you like. Other switches bring you radio programs. If you want dinner in your room, the porter brings you a table, and a waiter from the dining car serves you anything you want to eat. If your clothes need pressing, you give them to the porter. For a haircut, you just go to the barbershop or beauty parlor on the train.

All this is very much like living in a hotel on wheels, and it started about a hundred years ago when a man named George Pullman took a trip. The sleeping car he rode in was not really made for sleep. Along one side ran a row of hard triple-decker bunks with no springs. Mattresses were dirty, which wasn't surprising, because people went to bed with their shoes on. The bunks near the heating stove at one end got too hot, and the ones in the middle were too cold. A passenger who wanted light was wise to bring his own candles.

Pullman went to work on the idea of a real sleeper. By 1859 he had turned out a remodeled coach car that was a marvel of comfort. It still had its heating stove, and light came from candles in fancy chandeliers. But the beds in the lower tier were made up of springy car seats, and the soft upper berths could be raised or let down by pulleys.

The new sleeping car was so popular that George Pullman built some more. Many of the sleeping cars that railroads use today are made by the Pullman Company, and you must buy a special kind of ticket to ride in them. Others are made by the Budd Company and the American Car and Foundry Company.

In the old days, most Pullman cars looked very much alike. The seats were covered with prickly stuff in dark red or green. The woodwork was mostly dark colored or black. But now you see bright or unusual colors in many cars, and they often have pictures on the walls. Sometimes the pictures tell a story of a famous event that happened on the road or in the country it goes through. Santa Fe cars are decorated with scenes from Indian life or

in patterns taken from the beautiful sand paintings that the Indians make. Southern Pacific has the brands of famous ranches burned into the leather that covers the walls of its lounge cars.

As you walk through the train, you hardly notice that there are separate cars joined together. It wasn't always this way. Cars used to have an open platform at the end. The platforms were dangerous places to stand when the train lurched around a curve or jerked to a stop. Then somebody got the idea of enclosing the platforms with walls, doors, and a special kind of floor. People called these enclosed platforms "vestibules." The railroads were so proud of this invention that for many years they advertised trains made up of "vestibuled cars."

In those days, some trains reserved a car for women only. Some crack trains today have "family cars" for mothers and children. A playroom at one end is full of toys and books and games, perhaps with a slide and a place to show movies especially for children. At the other end of the car is a bathroom where mothers can bathe babies in baby tubs. A laundry machine washes diapers. The stewardess in the car will put baby's milk in a refrigerator and warm it up at mealtime.

Almost every day you read of something that railroads have added to keep people interested in riding on trains. One of the best ideas is the carefully planned schedule of the *Zephyr*, a crack train from Chicago to California, which travels through the least interesting country at night and beautiful high mountain country in the daytime.

A fast passenger train is a busy place. When you travel
on one, you'll notice a lot of different people working at
different jobs. Let's take a look at what they're doing.

The man you see most often, of course, is the conductor.
He takes the tickets and calls the stations. He is the one
who signals the engineer when it's time for the train to start.
If you haven't been able to get a ticket before you board

the train, the conductor will collect your fare and give you a receipt for it.

The conductor has special work to do when passengers are taking a long trip over several different railroads. A ticket for this kind of trip is a long strip of paper with

sections for each different road. Conductors must tear off the right slips and make records of them. In order to do all his paper work, the conductor on a crack train has his own little office with a desk in it. On ordinary passenger trains, his office is just any seat that happens to be empty.

The brakeman is the conductor's helper. He watches out when cars are being coupled onto the train or taken off. He helps passengers aboard and calls out stations, too.

The porter in the sleeping car has many kinds of work to do. He makes up the berths and takes care of all the little things that passengers ask for. He brings extra pillows. He shines shoes. He sees that the dressing rooms are kept neat and have plenty of towels and soap. He has to check all the laundry and see that soiled things get put off the train and clean things brought aboard.

The dining-car chef is like the chef in a restaurant, except that he must learn how to work in a very narrow kitchen. He has to organize all his pots and pans, tools, and foods so that he can get meals quickly without bumping into others. This means he must have a good disposition and the knack of getting along with other people. Cooking isn't his only job, either. He plans meals. He keeps a careful record of all the supplies in his galley, so that he won't run out of eggs or bacon or apple pie in the middle of a trip. And, of course, on very fancy trains he must know how to make all kinds of special dishes that passengers may order.

The chefs usually go to school to learn the special work they do on dining cars, as do the dining-car waiters.

The steward on the dining car is somewhat like the headwaiter in a restaurant. He shows people where to sit and collects the money for their meals. Along with the chef, he has to act as storekeeper for the diner. He orders everything that is needed to stock the galley shelves when the diner stops at its regular station for refills.

A train secretary, who may be either a man or a woman, does the same job as a secretary in an office. Suppose a passenger wants to write some letters. He asks the conductor for a dictating machine and talks into it. The secretary takes the record, plays it back, and types out the letters.

There are jobs for registered nurses on some trains, too. When children travel alone, the nurse takes care of them and tucks them into their berths at night. If a passenger has to take medicine, he tells the nurse and she sees that he gets it at the right time. When anyone gets sick on the train, she makes him comfortable and gives first aid until a doctor can be found.

If you take a long trip, you won't have the same conductor and brakeman all the way. They work during part of the trip, then get off and work on a returning train, so they can be home at the end of every day or two. (Engineers and firemen do this, too.)

Most of the other workers on the train don't get home so often. They may go all the way with the train, or at least a good deal farther than the rest of the crew. They have their own living quarters in a dormitory car toward the front of the train.

Altogether there may be as many as twenty-five people on a fast train whose job it is to make you comfortable.

Pysen Goes to Blueviken

by EDITH UNNERSTAD

illustrated by RICHARD SCARRY

PYSEN AND LITTLE O
ROW TO BLUEVIKEN

It was a Friday morning in November at the Larssons', two
flights up in the old house on West St. Per's Street in
Norrköping, Sweden.

"Usch, such slushy weather," said Mamma, as she pulled
up the shades in the Chicken Coop.

The Chicken Coop was what the family called the room of the two youngest ones. Pysen was five and Little O, three years old.

"Can't we go out?" they cried together.

"No, it is better for you to stay inside today," said Mamma. "I let Sotarn out a little while ago, and after half a minute he came in again, his fur completely soaked. What would you do outside in weather like this?"

"Play," said Pysen.

"Play," echoed Little O.

"You can play inside," called Knutte from the doorway, "but don't touch my things."

"Good morning to you, chickens," said Papa, peeking in.

"Morning," said Pysen. "What are we going to do all day, then?"

"Well, paint, for instance," said Papa. "Ask Dessi for paper and paint."

Dessi was seventeen. The moment she had finished her school work she would start painting.

But Dessi already was on her way down the stairs. Lasse, Knutte, Mirre and Rosalinda hurried after. They were all going to school. Then Papa left. He was going to his factory.

Pysen and Little O got out of bed. They dressed, ate their cereal and rye crisp with butter, and drank their milk.

And then, they didn't know what to do.

Sotarn, the Larssons' black cat, was sitting in the window licking his wet fur. Occasionally he would chase the rain drops trickling down on the outside of the window. He looked very annoyed when he couldn't catch them. The

rain was coming down so hard outside, you could scarcely see across the yard.

The mailman came, but there were only dull letters, not even a magazine with pictures. Usch, such a day!

Pysen went into the girls' room and looked for Dessi's paint box. But she had probably locked it up in her cupboard, because he couldn't find it.

Little O began dressing her dolls. That wasn't anything for Pysen. He stood around for a while, and—then—he thought of something.

"I know," he said. "Let's play boats."

Little O usually agreed to whatever Pysen suggested. And she especially loved to row. While playing boats, she and Pysen certainly must have rowed several miles.

"Let's play boats," she, too, agreed.

"Mamma," called Pysen, "can we have our boats?"

Mamma turned off the vacuum cleaner and brought the two enamelled washbasins out from the cupboard under the sink.

Four old wooden spoons, as usual, served as oars.

"Where are you going today?" she asked.

"To Blueviken," said Pysen.

"To Blueviken," said Little O.

"And then we are going to row to Möja," said Pysen.

"Möja," said Little O.

"And pick strawberries and fill the whole boat full," said Pysen.

"Full of strawberries," said Little O, and laughed, showing the dimples in her round cheeks.

"All right then, be off with you," said Mamma, "so I can get my cleaning done. Bring home a few strawberries for me, too."

"You'll get so many strawberries, the whole cellar will be full with jam," said Pysen.

Then they carried the two washbasins to Blueviken. Blueviken was the long hall which went through the entire house. There was a blue cork mat on the floor that made fine water.

Pysen and Little O sat down in their basins and began to row with their wooden spoons. If they rocked a tiny bit, first to one side, then to the other side, the basins would move forward with small jumps on the shiny blue mat.

Not everyone can row a washbasin, but Pysen and Little O had been at it for a long time. They were real experts. It is possible that the cork mat was a little the worse for wear, but Mamma never talked about that. No doubt she thought it was more important that her two youngest ones had fun.

And fun they had.

"High waves today," said Pysen, rowing and jerking and getting quite warm.

"But we aren't sinking," said Little O, struggling to keep up with him.

"Stop!" cried Pysen. "We forgot the food. We must row home again."

So they turned their boats around and rowed and rowed.

"Mamma," roared Pysen. "You didn't give us any food. We have to eat when we get to Möja, you know that."

Mama turned off the vacuum cleaner again and hurried out in the kitchen. She made two sandwiches and wrapped them in a piece of paper. As Pysen's boat approached the kitchen door, she tried to throw the package on board, but she missed. The package landed on the floor behind the boat.

"The foodbag fell into the sea," screamed Pysen.

"Excuse me, captain," said Mamma.

After a bit of trouble Pysen succeeded in saving it with one of his oars. And off they went again along Blueviken.

Little O's boat capsized once with a too wild jerk. But she was able to right it again. She didn't sink either; for Pysen helped her into the boat.

"You better be careful, you can't swim," he said.

"Yes, I am careful, I am," puffed Little O.

For a long time they rowed and rowed. Finally they arrived at Möja. Lasse's and Knutte's room at the end of Blueviken was Möja. Here they pulled the boats up on the beach and went ashore.

Lasse's desk became a tent. When Pysen and Little O sat under the desk they were inside the tent. There they made make-believe coffee, brought out their food, and ate their lunch. Later on they crawled out and picked strawberries on Lasse's couch, and loaded the boats to the brim. Then they rowed home and gave it all to Mamma.

The trip home went much faster than the journey out, for once in a while they would cheat a little and use their feet to help it along.

Mamma thanked them and said she would make the jam as soon as she had finished her cleaning. And never before had she seen such ripe red berries, she said.

All this talk about berries and jam made Pysen and Little O hungry, and Mamma had to give each of them a taste from the jar she kept in the pantry. Perhaps the nicest thing about those trips to Möja was that they always ended up with a taste of strawberry jam and a bit of cream. Strawberry jam is very good, especially if it comes with a little cream on it. And that was something which Mamma understood.

After a while the long hall stopped being Blueviken, and became the railroad between Norrköping and Stockholm.

Mamma said that they really ought not to play train when it was cleaning day. But since the weather was so bad, it probably couldn't be helped. Pysen and Little O gathered together the chairs and stools and lined them up to make a train in the long hall.

Little O was the engineer, and Pysen took the tickets and called out: "Nyköping! Vagnherad! Södertalje Södra!" And all the dolls and the bears and other animals were the passengers. Sotarn was supposed to be a passenger, too, but he jumped off when the train moved, so he and Mamma had to be stationmasters instead. Mamma came to the door

and waved the dust rag when the train was to leave, and Sotarn waved his tail. Once in a while, of course, he was stupid and crawled under the train and was almost run over.

After a while they were tired of playing train too, so they carried back all the chairs and the dolls and everything else, and picked up the tickets from the floor. Then Mamma told them to stay in the boys' room while she was cleaning the long hall and the Chicken Coop.

Knutte was twelve years old. He had a collection of stones, a stamp collection, a skeleton of a snake in a glass case, six blown-out eggs in a box and four knives in sheaths, hanging on the wall. Pysen and Little O never dared to touch Knutte's things, for then he became very angry. Lasse had lots of books. He was fourteen years old. He was always reading. He studied hard and read lots of books. In some of his books there were funny pictures. They couldn't cut those out, but it was fun to look at them anyway. Pysen and Little O were not afraid of touching Lasse's books. Each took one and began to look for funny pictures. But this time they just couldn't find any.

"We are reading, anyway," said Pysen. "We are reading just like Lasse. Let's both read this book, because it's nicer."

Neither of them knew how to read, but they were reading in their own way. Pysen actually had taught himself a few letters.

"This one is B," he said. "And that one is T."

"What's this one?" asked Little O, pointing to a big S.

"Don't know," said Pysen. "It looks like a top."

"I think it is a nop," said Little O.

"Yes, it must be a nop," said Pysen enthusiastically, "it looks like a nop."

Neither of them knew what a nop was. And, of course, a nop isn't anything. It isn't a word at all. But Little O had thought it up, and Pysen thought it sounded much funnier than a top.

"And that round ring is a big O, and that little ring is a little o," said Pysen.

"That's not so," said Little O. "That's not me."

"Yes, because Lasse said so," said Pysen. "And it looks like you, very, very much."

"But it doesn't have any eyes," said Little O. "I have two eyes, I have."

"We can draw your eyes in it," said Pysen.

Taking a pen from the desk he drew eyes in every little o he could find. Now Little O thought they looked more like her.

"Let's start reading," said Pysen.

And then he began. In a funny singsong way he said:

"Aboli
tjaboli
B, T, nop.
Big O
and little o.
Aboli
tjaboli
B, T, nop
Big O
and little o."

And Little O joined in. Each read a different page in the same book, sometimes holding it upside-down. But what did that matter? They were pointing with their little fingers, and feeling very happy, for now they felt they had learned to read.

"Aboli
tjaboli
B, T, nop
Big O
and little o."

Reading was lots of fun. They read the same thing over and over again.

When Mamma came in and said it was time to eat, they were still sitting there, reading aloud.

Mamma threw up her hands. As if she really was surprised.

134

"If you aren't sitting here reading!" she said.

"Aboli tjaboli," prattled Pysen and Little O proudly.

"But I don't quite understand what you are saying," said Mamma. "It doesn't sound like Swedish."

"We are reading English," said Pysen. "Exactly like Lasse. Listen: Isn't this English?"

"Aboli
tjaboli
B, T, nop
Big O
and little o."

"English," said Little O, importantly. "Aboli tjaboli . . ."

"What are we having to eat?" asked Pysen, closing the book so quickly that Little O almost had the tip of her nose pressed flat.

"Royaley
sausagey
scrambledy
eggs,
for big Pysen
and Little O,"

said Mamma.

"Oh good," said Pysen. "Do you know English, too?"

"A little," said Mamma.

"Easy it is," said Pysen.

"Easy," said Little O.

PYSEN GOES FOR HIS DUCK

"Where is my duck?" said Pysen. "Has anybody seen my duck?"

"Do, I didd't see it," answered Little O, who was in bed in the middle of the day because she had a cold and a stuffed-up nose.

"Can't you keep track of your own things?" said Knutte.

"No," said Pysen. "I mean yes. Somebody has taken him away."

"You probably did that yourself," said Mamma.

"Where did you have it the last time?" asked Mirre.

Pysen pondered a while.

"Don't know," he said. "But I want him. I need him tonight in the bathtub. Little O stepped on my boat and broke it."

"She couldn't help that," said Rosalinda. "You left it right in the middle of the floor. Can't you use the turtle instead?"

"That old washturtle isn't any fun," said Pysen.

"It is called a turtle, not a washturtle," corrected Knutte.

"He is called the washturtle," said Pysen, "because he gets so dirty I have to bathe him. But he has a hole in his stomach, so he can't swim. I want *my duck*."

"You will have to go and find it then," said Mamma. "But first you are going out a little bit, while the sun is shining. Help him on with his ski pants, Rosalinda!"

"Bake a sdoban for me," called out Little O.

"I'll make a snowman, yes, but where is my duck?" said Pysen stubbornly.

"I can't remember when I last saw it," said Mamma. "You probably took it out with you and left it some place."

"Maybe it is at Aunt Bella's," said Pysen and brightened up.

After he put on his jacket, cap and mittens, he went down to Aunt Bella's laundry on the first floor.

"Have you seen my duck, Aunt Bella?"

"No," said Aunt Bella, "not since last summer when we were out at the cottage. I wonder if you didn't leave it there?"

137

"Can we go and get it then?" asked Pysen eagerly.

"Oh my goodness, no. There is altogether too much snow in the country at this time, and it must be terribly cold in the cottage. We'll have to wait until spring."

Pysen looked downcast.

"The duck will be cold," he said. "Poor, poor little duck."

Aunt Bella said she didn't think that celluloid ducks ever felt the cold. And if Pysen would only be so good as to go out and play, he might taste her fresh raisin rolls as soon as she put the frosting on.

Pysen went over to the stable. Lasse was there, rubbing down the horses.

Yes, the Larssons kept horses. Two of them in fact. They had inherited them from a relative and couldn't think of ever parting with them. Although they only were a couple of heavy work horses, they had become a part of the family and the children had had many an amusing adventure with them. Papa Larsson used the horses for deliveries at his factory. And since Miss Breemer's house, where they now lived, had once had coaches for hire, there was a splendid stable which the Larssons now rented.

"Lasse," said Pysen, "you must harness Laban and Lotta and drive me to the cottage."

"To the cottage?" said Lasse. "Hardly, sonny. Laban and Lotta have been working since seven o'clock this morning, and they are tired now."

"Well, I must have my duck," said Pysen, "cause he is out at the cottage and getting cold."

"I'll get it on Sunday," said Lasse, "when Rosalinda and I go out there to ski."

"Yes, but I want him now," said Pysen determinedly.

But Lasse said it just couldn't be done. And when Lasse said no, he knew, there was no use asking again.

Pysen went out in the yard and began making a snowman for Little O. But it wasn't fun, for he couldn't stop thinking about his duck.

"Pysen," called Aunt Bella. "Come and get your rolls. How many do you want?"

"'Two," said Pysen. "No three. No four. No five rolls, please."

"Well, you never had a small appetite," said Aunt Bella and laughed. "Don't eat them all at once, though."

"Could I have them in a bag?" said Pysen.

He got his bag, bowing and thanking her politely for it. Then he went outdoors. He stood beside the half-finished snowman, thinking for a while.

Suddenly he set off across the yard and out through the big gate and on down the street. Since nobody cared about helping him, he was going to find his duck himself. He had gone on the bus to the cottage several times before, and he knew exactly where to board it.

Every time he had to cross a street, he stopped and hesitated. But the longing for the duck got the better of him and he went on.

At the bus stop a lady and two men were waiting. The lady was carrying a box and a pastry carton. One of the men was quite fat. He was holding a leash in his hand. Pysen stopped beside him, looking with interest at the leash.

"We only have a cat," he said.

"Well, cats are nice, too," said the fat man, smiling in a friendly fashion.

"Is your dog terribly fat, too?" inquired Pysen.

The gentleman burst out laughing.

"Well, he isn't exactly thin. He likes to eat like his master," he said.

Pysen turned to the lady with the pastry carton.

"I have rolls, too," he said, proudly showing his bag.

"Oh my oh my," she said, smiling, too.

Then the bus arrived. All four boarded it. Pysen sat down on the bench behind the driver. The man with the leash sat down beside Pysen.

"And where are you going?" he asked.

"To Aunt Bella's cottage," said Pysen. "I am going to get a duck there."

The fat man thought Pysen meant a real duck.

"That's fine," he said. "But are you big enough to carry a whole duck?"

"I can carry many many ducks," said Pysen. "Ducks aren't heavy. And I am strong, I am."

The fat gentleman looked a little bewildered. But just then the bus driver came for the fare.

"I don't have to pay, I am too little," said Pysen.

The driver saluted. He thought the fat gentleman was Pysen's papa, and then of course Pysen would go for nothing.

Once they started off, Pysen did what he always used to do when riding the bus. He helped the driver. He pretended to have a wheel in front of him, and a clutch and handbrakes next to it. He was holding out his hands steering his imaginary wheel. When the driver shifted gears, he, too, shifted, and when the driver put on the brakes, Pysen did the same thing.

The bag with the raisin rolls was in the way. It kept falling down on the floor all the time. Pysen held it out to the fat gentleman, and said: "You can hold it while I am driving. But you mustn't eat all the rolls."

The fat man laughed and said he would try not to do that, although those rolls smelled awfully good. So Pysen

generously said to him: "You can take one." The fat man said no, he better not do that. But Pysen said: "Yes, go ahead and eat. They are my own rolls, and I can give them away, if I want to, can't I?"

"Well, thank you," said the fat gentleman and helped himself to a raisin roll from the bag. "Now, tell me, you are going to be a bus driver when you grow up, aren't you?"

"I am going to have a laundry," said Pysen curtly. "I shall have one two three four five mangles. Electric ones. But—I don't have time to talk now. I must drive."

And with renewed effort he drove on. When the gentleman had eaten the roll he said: "Is it permissible to disturb the assistant driver and tell him that it tasted wonderful?"

Pysen just drove on looking terribly busy. But he was eyeing his seatmate a little uneasily as he sat there rustling the bag. Wonder if he was thinking about taking more than one roll?

Now and then the bus made a stop. Pysen pulled the handbrake tight. Some more passengers got on. One of them was a lady Mamma used to buy eggs from in summertime. But Pysen had no time for her. He had to watch so the bus didn't end up in the ditch in some of the bends on the road.

"Here is where I get off," said the fat man, as they stopped at a cross road. "Goodbye, and thank you for the roll. Take a look in the bag when you get time."

"Adjö," said Pysen, wondering what he meant. Had he taken another roll?

The fat man put the bag on the seat and got off. The driver turned to Pysen and asked him if he weren't getting off here also. But the fat gentleman down on the road laughed, and waving his leash he called out:

"No, he is going to Aunt Bella's cottage to get a duck."

"Yes," said Pysen, "and I know where to get off. There is a bush there, all covered with pink flowers."

The driver laughed and all the passengers joined in. Most of them thought that the fat gentleman was Pysen's papa, and that someone was waiting for the boy at Aunt Bella's cottage. The egg lady was talking about where the cottage was and where the bus driver was to let him off. Pysen only gripped his imaginary wheel harder and drove on.

After a while his stop came. At first he didn't know where he was, because he didn't see any pink flowers, only snow and snow-covered bushes and trees. But then he discovered the gate to Miss Breemer's summer place. Two white suns were painted on it. He had always thought it the finest gate in the world. Now he knew where to go.

The road to the cottage was covered with snow. But Pysen plodded on in his heavy boots, and thought it was a lot of fun, although it took him some time to get there. The sun was shining and the snow was as soft as cotton, and he wasn't cold at all.

There was the cottage. There was snow on the stairs, and a lot of snow hanging down from the roof. The chimney had on a white cap.

Aunt Bella owned the cottage, but all the Larssons stayed there in the summer time, swimming, sailing and rowing at Brueviken, or "Blueviken," as the children called it.

144

Pysen climbed up the stairs and tried to open the door. It was locked. He shook and twisted the doorknob, and knocked at the door, but nothing helped. That made him so angry he tried to kick the door open, but that only hurt his toes.

"Silly, silly door," he said, "let me in so I can get my duck."

But the door wasn't to be persuaded, and for a moment he felt so downhearted he started to cry. And then he remembered his raisin rolls. Sweeping away a little snow with his mitten, he sat down and opened his bag. But what

was this? Two large chocolate bars on top of the rolls. Milk chocolate.

"Magic," cried Pysen in delight.

Once in a while Lasse used to make magic for him, but who in the world could have made this? Lasse hadn't even seen the bag.

Pysen ate two rolls and a chocolate bar. They tasted wonderful. Now he started to look around. Yes, there was the woodshed, and down there the pier. But where was *Rudolfina*, the Larsson children's beloved old boat? She was not at her usual place between the pier and the buoy. He really was alarmed now. Had someone been there and stolen *Rudolfina?*

And then, like a streak of lightning it struck him. The duck! It wasn't in the cottage at all. Why, it was on board *Rudolfina*. Now he remembered. And *Rudolfina* was gone and the duck with it.

First he thought only about getting home to Mamma and Papa and all the others to tell them about this terrible thing. But somehow he couldn't quite understand it yet. He just had to look a little closer. He waded down to the pier in the loose snow which reached far above his knees.

There lay the boats, up and down the beach, but no *Rudolfina*. And there wasn't any sea either, not a real sea. Blueviken looked exactly like land with a lot of snow on. And out there was Limpan, the little islet with the boat yard, and it, too, was covered with snow.

But look—there—yes, there was *Rudolfina* after all! Out on Limpan. In the big shed among all the other boats.

"Oh, how dumb I was," cried Pysen loudly.

He was feeling both happy and foolish because now he remembered that Papa and Lasse had gone across to Limpan with *Rudolfina* and had returned with only the skiff. They had said that *Rudolfina* was going to be laid up for the winter.

But, then, of course, the duck was out on Limpan, too. That was worse. He just had to have the duck, of course.

The paper bag broke. Pysen stuffed the chocolate bar in his pocket and took a roll in each hand. Then he stepped out on the ice. It crackled under his boots and it was so much fun when the ice broke into a thousand small tinkling pieces. But he had no time to stand there. The duck! He began plodding out on the ice. The dark tracks which his boots made in the snow were immediately filled with water.

A little more than half way to Limpan he spotted, coming straight towards him, a tug with two barges, a heavy black column of smoke pouring out of the chimney. Afraid that it might run him down, Pysen raced on towards Limpan as fast as he could, and reached land just as the tug passed by. He stood there looking at it, how it broke the smooth white cover over the water and how ice and snow breaking into a thousand pieces were flung around the prow. There were two men on board, and they waved

and shouted something to him. He couldn't hear what they were saying, but he waved back with the roll. The ice cracked and crashed, and after the last barge had passed, there was a black stripe with open water. This was real sea, at least, with ice on. Well, that's what he had thought, the whole Blueviken couldn't just go and disappear completely.

He walked up to *Rudolfina* where she lay propped up under a shelter without walls. A ladder, fortunately, was leaning against the side of the boat. With the last roll between his teeth Pysen climbed on board. The cabin door was unlocked, but Pysen's hands were too small to get it open. The door had swelled, and it was stuck like a sugary cork in a bottle. He wasn't going to give up, though. He wanted his duck. Climbing around the cabin, he discovered the hatch. He had better luck here. Jerking it open he climbed down into the front of the boat. It was quite dark and damp down there, and the cabin wasn't any lighter, for the two small round windows didn't let in much light.

Pysen crept forward to his old bunk and stuck his hand in the box under the bed where the life belts were. At first he didn't find anything. Then he pulled off his mitten, and now he could feel something. It was something soft: Oh, Mirre's panholders in which he had put the duck to bed. And there was something cold and smooth. THE

DUCK! Finally. His own old wonderful little duck!

Pulling out the duck he patted it and held it up against his cheek. Poor duck, how cold it was. Like ice. He crawled up in the canvas bunk and put the duck under his coat.

"I am only going to warm you up a little, then we'll go home," he whispered, yawning widely. He was quite tired after his long jaunt, and didn't realize that his head began to nod. Before he knew it, his eyes closed.

Just as he fell asleep the pale winter sun slid behind the pine trees outside and dusk came.

At home nobody was particularly worried when Pysen didn't appear for dinner. He probably had gone to visit some of the neighbors, they thought. Mamma rang the cowbell out through the kitchen window, and that bell could be heard all over the yard. When Pysen still didn't show up, his brothers and sisters were all sent out to look for him. But he wasn't at Aunt Bella's or at any of the neighbors'.

Then they were very worried. Aunt Bella and Lasse recalled that Pysen had wanted them to go to the cottage with him.

"He's gone out there to get that old duck, I think," said Aunt Bella.

"He must have gone on the bus, then," said Lasse.

Papa telephoned the bus station. There they answered that, as far as they knew, no five-year-old had taken the bus today, but they were going to inquire further. A little while later a bus driver called back saying that a small boy in the company of a stout gentleman had ridden with him, and might he possibly be the one?

"Did he have on a white hood and blue jacket?" cried Mamma. "That was Pysen. Where did he go?"

A few minutes later Papa and Lasse were on their way out to the cottage in a taxi. They carried flashlights and blankets and a Thermos bottle with hot milk.

He'll be all right, they said at home, trying to comfort one another. He can't have gone off into the woods, now when there is so much snow; we needn't be afraid he has gone astray.

But, just the same, they were worried, although they didn't want to let on.

Papa and Lasse and the taxi driver followed the tracks of the small boots from the main road to the cottage. In the light from the flashlights they saw that Pysen had been sitting on the front steps, and below the steps they found the wrappings from the chocolate bar. But they also saw with growing fear that the tracks went down to the beach and further out on the ice.

"Hello, Pysen, where are you?" called Papa, swinging the flashlight.

But nobody answered. Papa tried the ice.

"Pysen isn't so heavy," he said anxiously, "but this thin ice won't hold a grown person."

Lasse wanted to try it anyway, but Papa held him back.

"The rowboat," he said. "Hurry, we can set out the rowboat, and push it in front of us."

All three helped in turning the boat and getting it out on the ice. The taxi driver stayed on the beach, but Papa and Lasse pushed the boat in front of them, following the tracks. Once in a while they broke through. Once Lasse sank down all the way to his waist, but pulled himself up again, thanks to the boat. It was terribly slow, they thought. And any moment they expected the tracks to lead to a hole in the ice. Suddenly Lasse stopped.

"The steam boat channel," he cried, seeing the black shiny edge glittering in the light from the flashlight. "Papa, the tracks are stopping here."

Papa didn't say a word, only continued to push the boat towards the channel. Stopping at the edge, they let the flashlight play over the dark silent water.

"But look—oh look there," shouted Lasse and pointed with his finger. "The tracks continue on the other side. Good, he made it across! But how could that happen?"

"Well, thank God," said Papa. "The steamer must have made the channel afterwards. And now, Lasse, we must try to get across. You climb into the boat and I'll push it out."

The ice on both sides of the channel broke under the boat, but somehow they managed to get across and ashore on Limpan. They followed Pysen's tracks.

"He has been at the boat shed," said Papa.

"He has gone to *Rudolfina*, because the tracks are leading to it but not away from it," said Lasse, who was a couple of steps ahead of Papa.

When Papa and Lasse with a loud crash managed to get the door open, Pysen sat up in the bunk, shivering and blinking, bewildered by the flashlight. He didn't realize at first where he was, but it soon became clear to him. He pulled out the duck from under his jacket and held it up to Lasse.

"I found him," he said, delighted. "Look, my duck."

"Oh, Pysen," said Papa, his voice sounding mighty peculiar, as he sat down beside his youngest son. "How could you think of doing anything as crazy as this?"

"I only came to get my duck," said Pysen.

Lasse brought out the Thermos bottle and poured some warm milk for his little brother.

"But how did you dare to walk on such thin ice?" he asked.

"Pooh," said Pysen gulping and drinking, "that wasn't so dangerous. The ice was full of tracks."

"Tracks," said Papa, patting and rubbing Pysen's back, "What kind of tracks?"

"Crow tracks," said Pysen lightly.

Papa and Lasse looked at one another. He and the crows, they were thinking.

"Pysen," said Papa seriously, "listen to what I say. You must never do such a thing again, because it is very dangerous. Don't ever go away like this, and don't ever go out on the ice alone."

"No-o," said Pysen, "but I couldn't let my duck stay out here and get cold."

When Pysen told about what happened later that evening, it sounded about like this:

"Then I and my duck got to go in our boat on the ice. And Papa and Lasse pushed us, and sometimes they slid down in the water, but they came up again. And then we drove home in a car, but I didn't get to drive, for they wrapped me up in blankets so I couldn't drive. And we forgot one of the mittens on *Rudolfina*, and then I had steak and dessert and all the girls came and fussed and wanted to kiss me. But I said, don't, and only Mamma got to kiss me a little on the hair. And then I took a bath with my duck for a long long time, and he was swimming much better than that washturtle."

Well, both Papa and Lasse came down with colds after the trip. But not Pysen, oh no, not he. As Mamma said, "Nothing affects that boy."

Let's Go to Colombia

Colombia is the only country in South America with a coastline along both the Atlantic and Pacific Oceans. Beyond the coastal lowlands stand the towering Andes Mountains which split into three separate ranges. Because Colombia has enough rainfall and differences in altitude—lowlands, fertile inland valleys, and vast plains—she can produce a variety of crops. Colombian farmers grow bananas and other tropical fruit, rice, cotton, sugar cane, coffee, grain, and potatoes. On the plains cattle are bred.

Colombia's progress has been slowed by old-fashioned farming methods and by the problems of transporting her mineral and agricultural products to markets. Her rich land yields a fortune in platinum, gold, gem emeralds, valuable trees, and petroleum, but most of her great mineral resources are still untapped.

The coast of Colombia was one of the first places on the South American continent visited by Spanish explorers. The Spaniards conquered the Indian tribes and ruled the land until the natives began to revolt in the late eighteenth century. Then in 1819 Simon Bolivar liberated the territory and set up the Republic of Gran Colombia which included parts of Ecuador and Venezuela. Later these parts broke off and Colombia became its present size. Colombia has had her share of trouble in government, but her history is not as full of revolutions and dictatorships as other South American republics. Today she is one of the most democratic South American nations. Her future looks bright.